Hip Hip Hooray for SCHOOL!

©2007 Learning Horizons, Inc., 5301 Grant Ave., Cleveland, OH 44125. Made in U.S.A.
Visit us at: **www.learninghorizons.com**

Hip Hip Hooray for School!

Table of Contents

Discovering Letter Sounds

Learn About Language

Know Your Numbers

Learn About Math

DISCOVERING
LETTER SOUNDS

You are invited to come on a letter sound adventure with Elmo and the other Sesame Street friends!

LEARN TO:

- ◆ Identify beginning letter sounds
- ◆ Recognize uppercase and lowercase letters
- ◆ Find sounds that are the same

Family Activities

Letter Day Drawing

Choose a "letter of the day" and write it on a sheet of paper. Throughout the day, encourage your child to listen for words that begin with that letter sound. When he hears the letter sound, help him to draw a picture and/or write the corresponding word around the letter. For example, if the "letter of the day" is **D**, make the letter sound together "**D-D-D-D**." Then help your child to identify **D** words such as: **dog**, **desk**, **door**, **donut**, and **dime**. Display all of his "letter of the day" masterpieces and keep adding to them every day!

What Doesn't Belong?

Choose a letter and gather 4 items that begin with that letter. For example, if the letter is **S**, you might collect **soap**, **spoon**, **sock**, and **sticker**. Then choose an item that does not begin with the **s** sound (like a **top**, a **doll**, or a **mitten**) and place it with the items. Mix the items up and encourage your child to choose what doesn't belong by selecting the item that does not start with the **s** sound. Help her by stressing the beginning letter sound for each object.

Letter Sound Match

Have your child collect 4 toys or other items from around your home (like a **b**all, a **c**ar, a **t**issue, and a **d**oll) and place them on the table or floor. With small slips of paper or individual sticky notes, write the letter that stands for the beginning letter sound of each word (like **b**, **c**, **t**, **d**). Have your child say the name of each item and encourage him to find the letter that matches the beginning letter sound. Find new items and make new letter cards, then play again!

Make A B-Brown Bag

Use a brown grocery bag and old newspaper pages or your own drawings. Help your child to decorate the outside of the bag with **b** words (like **big**, **boo**, **bam**, **blast**, **boogie**) or **b** pictures (like **boat**, **bag**, **bat**, **ball**, **bear**). You might choose to use **blue**, **brown**, or **black** colors to add decorations. Then send your child on a hunt to find things in your home that begin with the letter **b** (like a **ball**, **boot**, **banana**, or **bowl**) and have him put the items in the B-Brown Bag. You can try this with other letters, too!

Letter Sound Parade

Choose a letter to start the parade and emphasize the letter sound for your child. March around while you sing the letter sound over and over. Add silly words that begin with the same letter sound. For example, if the letter is **G**, you might sing, "**G-G-G-G-Great Green Gobbly Gabbly Goobly Goo, Go G-G-G**." Choose another letter and sing again. Add some of her friends to the parade, dress up in silly costumes, carry homemade instruments if you wish, and keep marching!

6

m
milk

Cookie Monster drinks milk with his cookies. **Milk** begins with the letter **m** sound.

 Say the name of each picture. Circle the objects whose names begin with the letter **m** sound.

S
sand

Snuffy has fun in the sand.
Sand begins with the letter **s** sound.

  Say the name of each picture. Color the ones whose names begin with the letter **s** sound.

Explore More

Encourage your child to look through old magazines for pictures that begin with the same letter sound as his name. Help your child cut out the pictures and glue or tape them to a piece of paper, making a collage for that letter. For example, a boy named Sam might create an **S** collage using pictures of a **sun**, **sandwich**, **seal**, and **suit**.

a
apple

Zoe has an apple.
Apple begins with the letter **a** sound.

  Say the name of each picture. Circle the objects whose names begin with the letter **a** sound.

b
book

Bert reads a book about bears.
Book begins with the letter **b** sound.

 Say the name of each picture. Color the ones that begin with the letter **b** sound.

10

Telly plays the tuba.
Tuba begins with the letter **t** sound.

 Say the name of each picture. Circle the things that begin with the letter **t** sound.

Elmo eats an egg for breakfast.
Egg begins with the letter **e** sound.

 Say the name of each picture. Color the ones that begin with the letter **e** sound.

Hip Hip Hooray for School! Discovering Letter Sounds

SESAME STREET

Help Big Bird find Radar.

Draw the path that Big Bird should follow. The correct path has pictures whose names begin with the letter **b** sound.

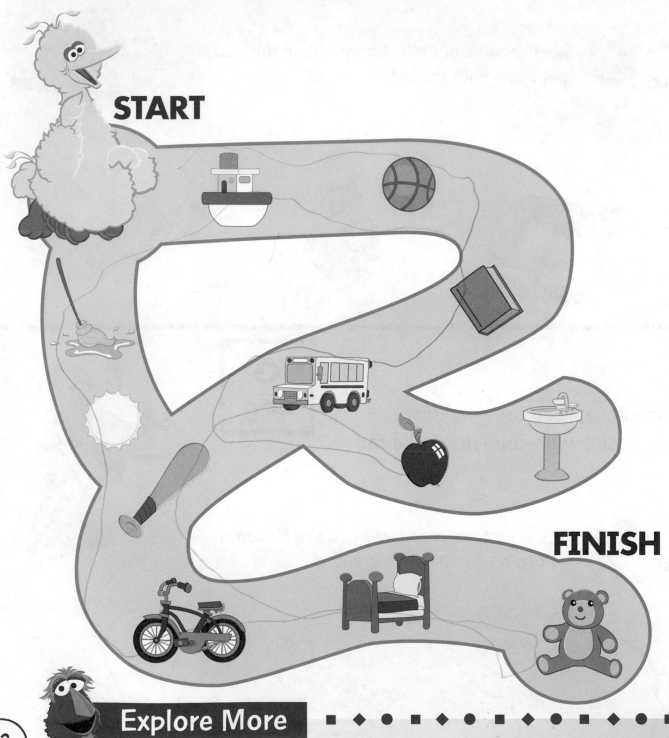

START

FINISH

Explore More

Invite your child to go on a letter sound scavenger hunt with you. Look for objects in your home that begin with one of the letter sounds your child has learned. Put the objects you find on a table and encourage your child to talk about them.

12

h
hat

Herry Monster has a party hat.
Hat begins with the letter **h** sound.

  Say the name of each picture. Circle the ones
that begin with the letter **h** sound.

Rosita rests in her robe.
Robe begins with the letter **r** sound.

  Say the name of each picture. Color the ones
that begin with the letter **r** sound.

i
ill

Ernie is feeling ill.
Ill begins with the letter **i** sound.

 Say the name of each picture. Circle the ones that begin with the letter **i** sound.

15

Dorothy is Elmo's favorite fish.
Fish begins with the letter **f** sound.

  Say the name of each picture. Color the ones that begin with the letter **f** sound.

x
x-ray

Baby Bear has an x-ray.
X-ray begins with the letter **x** sound.

  Say the name of each picture. Color the one that begins with the letter **x** sound.

l
lemonade

Lemonade
5¢

Telly is selling lemonade.
Lemonade begins with the letter **l** sound.

 Say the name of each picture. Circle the ones that begin
with the letter **l** sound.

17

Explore More

Look at a family photo album with your child. Talk about the people and things you
see in the pictures. As you name family members and friends, encourage your child
to say the beginning sound of each person's name.

Elmo's rockets have pictures on them!

  Say the names of the pictures. Color two pictures on each rocket whose names begin with the same sound.

d
dog

Barkley the Dog digs in the dirt.
Dog begins with the letter **d** sound.

  Say the name of each picture. Circle the ones that begin with the letter **d** sound.

19

C
cookie

Cookie Monster can always find a cookie.
Cookie begins with the letter **c** sound.

 Say the name of each picture. Color the ones that begin with the letter **c** sound.

20

o
orange

Oscar eats an orange.
Orange begins with the letter **o** sound.

  Say the name of each picture. Circle the ones that begin with the letter **o** sound.

k
kitten

Ernie feeds the kitten.
Kitten begins with the letter **k** sound.

  Say the name of each picture. Color the ones that begin with the letter **k** sound.

 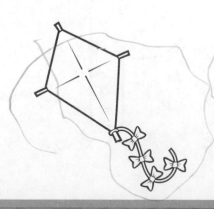 

21

The Count is holding a musical note.
Note begins with the letter **n** sound.

  Say the name of each picture. Color the ones that begin with the letter **n** sound.

22

 **g**
guitar

Grover can play the guitar.
Guitar begins with the letter **g** sound.

  Say the name of each picture. Circle the ones that begin with the letter **g** sound.

---

w
waffle

Slimey the Worm wants a waffle.
Waffle begins with the letter **w** sound.

 Say the name of each picture. Color the ones that begin with the letter **w** sound.

  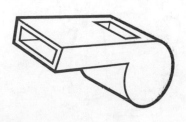

Ernie has a jar of jelly.
Jar begins with the letter **j** sound.

  Say the name of each picture. Circle the ones that begin with the letter **j** sound.

u
umbrella

The Twiddle Bug is under the umbrella.
Umbrella begins with the letter **u** sound.

  Say the name of each picture. Color the ones that begin with the letter **u** sound.

 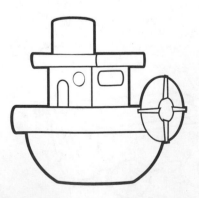 

 Hip Hip Hooray for School Discovering Letter Sounds

Cookie Monster likes to play tic-tac-toe.

Draw a line through three pictures on each
board whose names begin with the same sound.

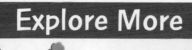

Explore More

Each day on Sesame Street, Cookie Monster picks a letter of the day.
Encourage your child to pick a letter of the day at home, too! Plan
activities for the day that correspond with the letter. For example, on
W day you can **water** the plants, take a **walk**, or make **waffles**.

25

p
pie

Prairie Dawn baked a peach pie.
Pie begins with the letter **p** sound.

 Say the name of each picture. Circle the ones that begin with the letter **p** sound.

| **q**
| **queen** |

Rosita looks like a queen.
Queen begins with the letter **q** sound.

 Say the name of each picture. Circle the ones
that begin with the letter **q** sound.

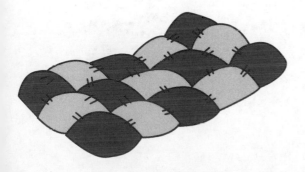

v
vase

Grover puts flowers in a vase.
Vase begins with the letter **v** sound.

  Say the name of each picture. Circle the ones that begin with the letter **v** sound.

Bert likes to play with a yo-yo.
Yo-yo begins with the letter **y** sound.

  Say the name of each picture. Circle the ones that begin with the letter **y** sound.

Zoe sees a zebra at the zoo.
Zebra begins with the letter **z** sound.

Say the name of each picture. Color the ones that begin with the letter **z** sound.

29

Big Bird loves to fly kites!

Look at the letter next to each kite. Color the kite if the picture begins with the same letter sound.

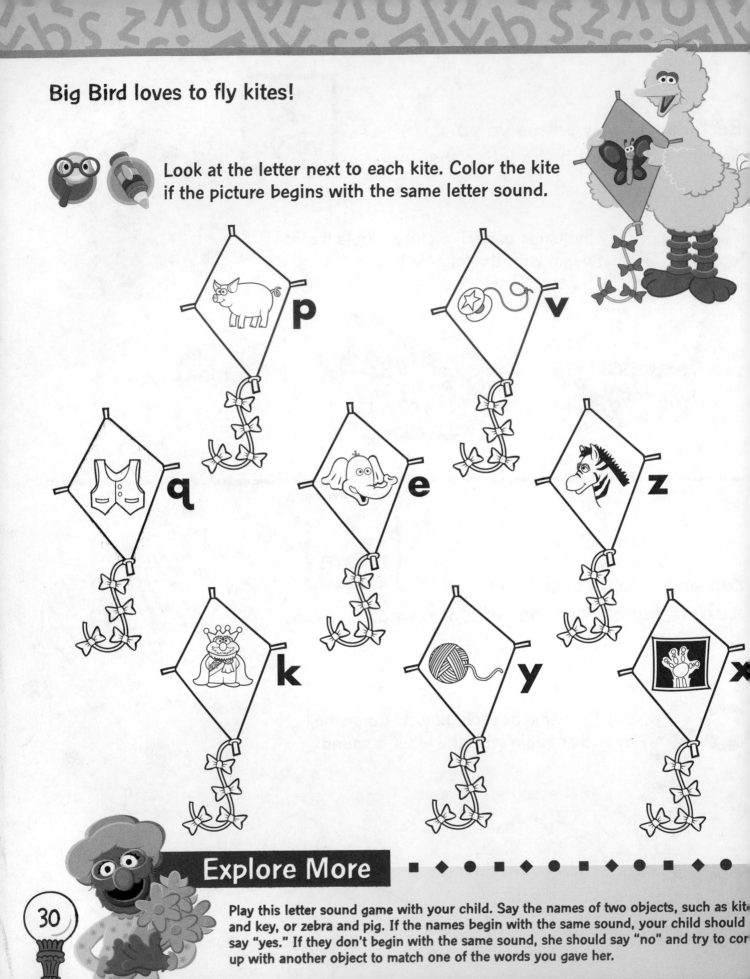

Explore More

Play this letter sound game with your child. Say the names of two objects, such as kit and key, or zebra and pig. If the names begin with the same sound, your child should say "yes." If they don't begin with the same sound, she should say "no" and try to co up with another object to match one of the words you gave her.

Learn About
LANGUAGE

Big Bird needs your help understanding vowels, making rhymes, and building words, so get your thinking cap on!

LEARN TO:
- Recognize letters
- Rhyme
- Understand short and long vowel sounds
- Identify consonant sounds
- Build words

red

big

blue

fish

Family Activities

What's In A Name?
Write the letters of your child's name on small slips of paper and place them in the correct order on a table or the floor. Scramble the letters up and have her place them back in the correct order. (For a younger child, write her entire name on a sheet of paper and let her use that as a reference for matching the letters.) Then encourage her to go on a letter hunt in your home to find all of the letters in her name. Give hints about where she can look, like on boxes, cans, clothing, and books. Encourage her to take the slips of paper with her on the hunt for easier matching.

Where's My Match?
Collect a clean set of bottle caps, or plastic lids. With a marker, write a lowercase letter on one lid, and the uppercase letter partner on another lid. Encourage your child to match the letter partners together. Add more letter partners and play again! For a challenge, turn the lids facedown and play a game of concentration. Have your child turn over two lids at a time in order to try and find a letter partner match.

First Letter
Blow up a beach ball for your child and practice hitting or throwing the ball back and forth. Give a few examples of words that start with the letter **r** and be sure to emphasize the **r** sound as you say the words. You may want to use the following words as examples: **rat, rip, rug, run, race, red, row**, and **real**. See if your child can think of a word each time he hits the ball back to you. Change the letter and play again!

Rhyme This Time
Take a trip to the local library and help your child find books that contain poems or rhymes. As you read, have your child guess the rhyme that completes the next line or sentence. Encourage her to make up her own rhymes and poems, too. You may want to begin with simple **short vowel** words (like **cat, top, pet, hit, sun, big, log, hot**) and then move on to **long vowel** words (like **team, kite, bean, take, bone, tune**).

Short Vowel Words
Write down all the vowels and review their short sounds. Choose a vowel sound and write the letter several times down the middle of a piece of paper. Encourage your child to choose a beginning letter and an ending letter. Then write the letters and sound out the new words. For example, if the middle letter is **o**, your child might choose to add the letter **n** at the beginning of the word and a **t** at the end to make the word **not**. Silly nonsense words are fun in this game, too!

32

Looking for Letters

Big Bird is looking for letters in the kitchen.

 Find and circle each letter hidden in the picture.

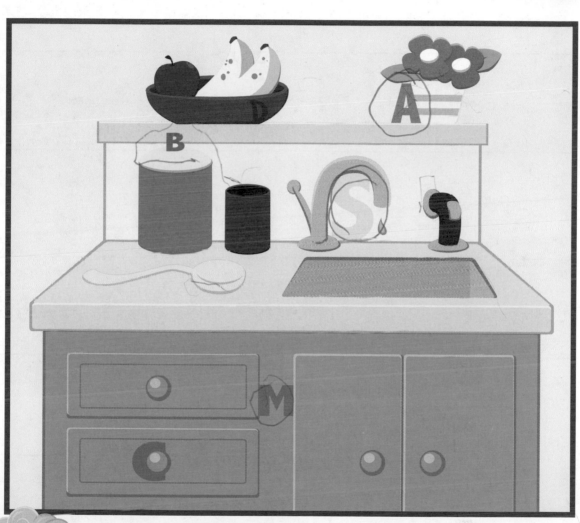

Explore More

Write the letters in your child's name on a piece of paper. Point to each letter and help your child identify each letter. Help your child create letters with different tools like chalk, crayons, markers, or colored pencils. Try using different kinds of paper, like lined paper, graph paper, poster board, or cardboard. Encourage your child to find letters around your home.

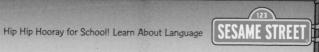

(33)

Big Bird loves learning the ABCs! The big letters in the alphabet are called uppercase letters. The small letters are called lowercase letters.

  Say the name of each alphabet letter. Then trace all of the letters.

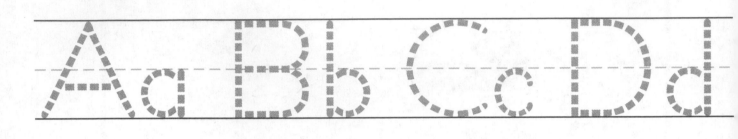

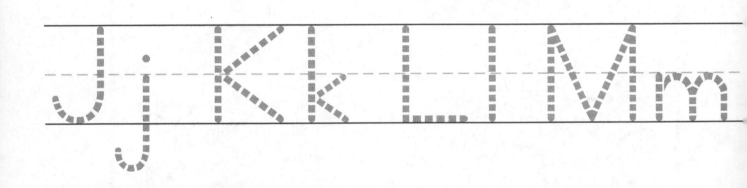

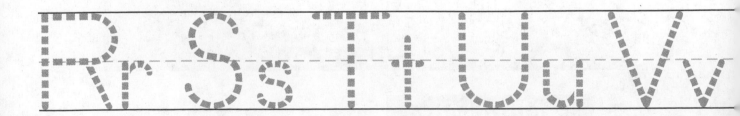

Ee Ff Gg Hh Ii

Nn Oo Pp Qq

Ww Xx Yy Zz

Hip Hip Hooray for School! Learn About Language

SESAME STREET

Big R, Little r

An uppercase letter and its matching lowercase letter
are called letter partners. **R** and **r** are letter partners.
Big Bird and Radar are holding the letter partners.

Draw a line from each uppercase letter
to its lowercase letter partner.

If you need help, look on pages 2 and 3 for the letter partners.

k
h
i

H

u
x
q

U

j
b
t

T

W

w
c
y

z
e
d

D

F

l
g
f

36

Socks and More Socks

B and **b** are letter partners. Look!
Big Bird has letter partners on his socks.

 Color each pair of socks that has letter partners.

B
b
S
s
n
G

m
K
P
p
a
V

e
E
g
F
J
j

Hip Hip Hooray for School! Learn About Language   SESAME STREET

Bring on the Books

Big Bird and Bert like to read books!
Book begins with the letter **b** sound.

  Point to each picture and say its name. Repeat the beginning sound that starts the name of each picture.

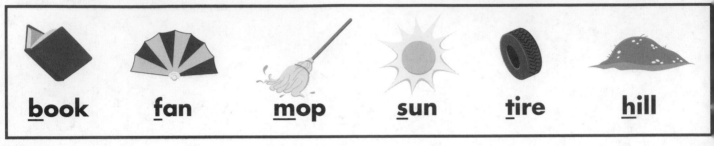

book   **f**an   **m**op   **s**un   **t**ire   **h**ill

 Look at each picture and say its name.
Circle the letter that stands for the beginning sound.

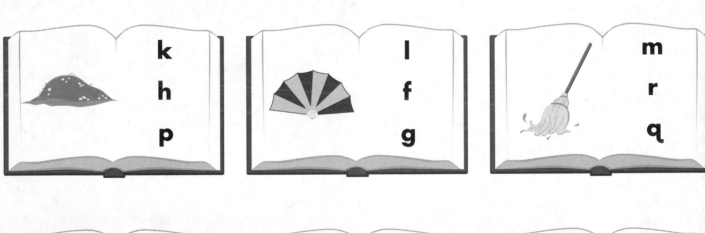

k
h
p

l
f
g

m
r
q

b
l
j

v
n
s

c
t
d

Snoozing on the Log

Big Bird and Elmo lie on a log.
Log begins with the letter **l** sound.

  Point to each picture and say its name. Repeat the beginning sound that starts the name of each picture.

log   **d**og   **c**at   **n**est   **w**eb

  Look at each picture and say its name. Circle the picture if its name begins with the letter sound at the beginning of the row.

d

c

n

w

39

Big Bird and Prairie Dawn picked plenty of peaches.
Peach begins with the letter **p** sound.

  Point to each picture and say its name.
Repeat the beginning sound that starts the name of each picture.

| **p**ot | **r**ug | **k**ing | **j**am | **v**ase | **y**ak |

 Look at each picture and say its name. Circle the letter that stands
for the same beginning sound. Write the letter to finish each word.

k **y**

king

w **p**

ot

j **q**

am

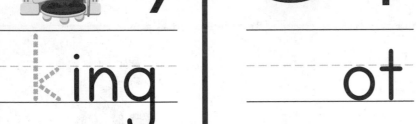

r **s**

ug

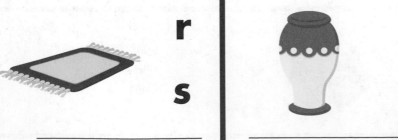

v **k**

ase

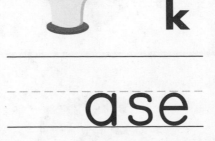 

g **y**

ak

Ham It Up

Big Bird loves to make ham sandwiches.
Ham ends with the letter **m** sound.

 Say the name of each picture. Repeat the sound of the last letter that you hear in the word.

Color each picture whose name has the same ending letter sound as the first picture in each row.

bu_s_  |  gas |  |

ca_t_  |  |  |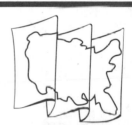

tu_b_  |  | 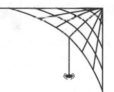 |

mai_l_  | 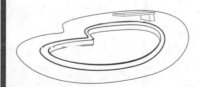 |  |

Explore More

Help your child cut out pictures of different things, such as toys, foods, or animals from newspaper and grocery store ads. Together, sort the pictures into groups that end with the same letter sound.

41

 SESAME STREET

Singing in the Sun

Big Bird and Radar sing in the sun.
Sun ends with the letter **n** sound.

 Say the name of each picture. Draw a line from each picture to the letter that stands for its ending sound.

r

n

p

x

g

p

x

g

k

n

Time to Review

The bus buzzed by Big Bird.
Bus begins with the letter **b** sound and ends with the letter **s** sound.

 Say the name of each picture. Write the letter for the beginning sound. Then, write the letter for the ending sound.

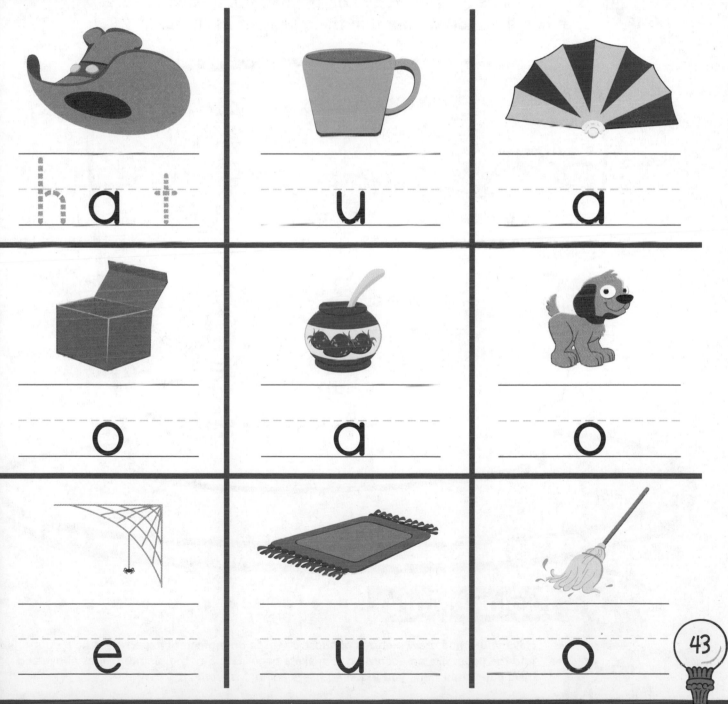

h **a** t	u	a
o	**a**	o
e	u	o

Hats, Hats, Hats

Big Bird has too many hats.
Hat has the short **a** sound in the middle.

  Say the name of each picture on the hat. Color each picture that has the short **a** sound in the middle of its name.

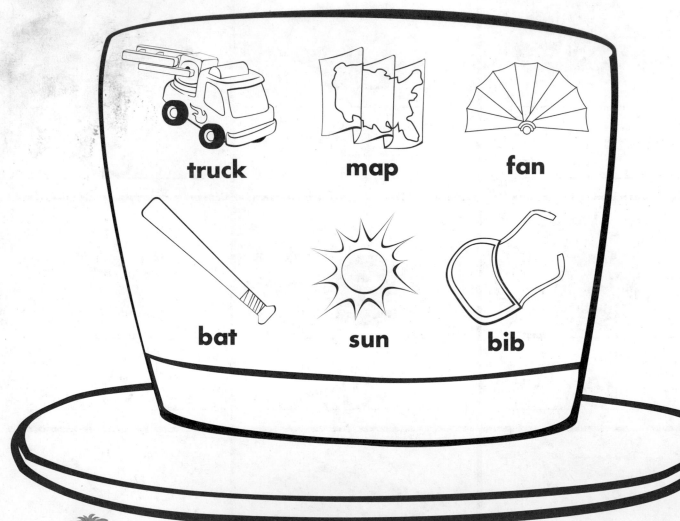

truck

map

fan

bat

sun

bib

Explore More ■ ◆ ● ● ◆ ■ ● ● ◆ ■

Have your child draw pictures of short **a** words on a piece of paper. Then help your child fold the paper like an accordion to make a paper fan. Say the picture names above and have your child "fan" you when he hears a short **a** word.

Hip Hip Hooray for School! Learn About Language

Bats, Bats, Bats

Big Bird is counting bats!
Bat has the short **a** sound in the middle.

  Say the name of each picture. Write **a** on the line if the picture name has the short **a** sound in the middle.

_____

a

_____

- - - - - - -

_____

- - - - - - -

_____

- - - - - - -

_____

- - - - - - -

_____

- - - - - - -

Hip Hip Hooray for School! Learn About Language

SESAME STREET

Red from Head to Toe

Big Bird and Elmo are dressed in red.
Red has the short **e** sound in the middle.

  Say the name of each picture. Color the picture **red** if the picture name has the short **e** sound.

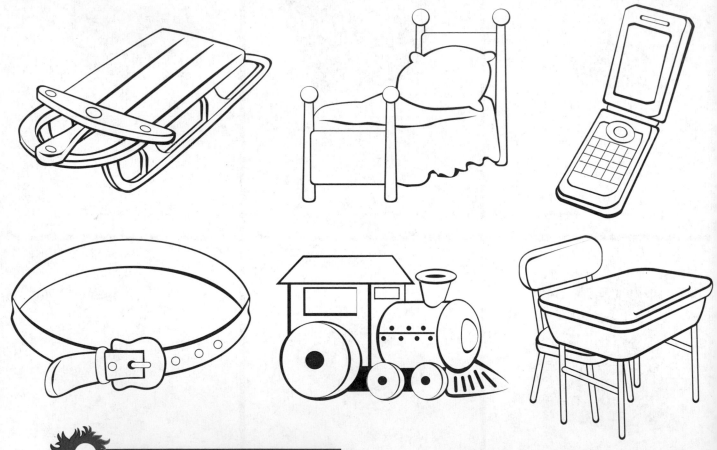

 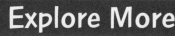 ## Explore More ◆ ◆ ◆ ◆ ◆ ◆ ◆ ◆ ◆ ◆ ◆

Get ready, get set, go! Help your child find objects in your home whose names have the short **e** sound. Then count how many of the items are red. Try this with other letter sounds, too.

46

Yes, It Smells Swell!

Oscar thinks everything smells swell. **Smell** has the short **e** sound in the middle.

  Say the name of each picture. Write **e** on the line if the picture name has the short **e** sound.

SESAME STREET

Gone Fishing

Big Bird caught a fish.
Fish has the short **i** sound in the middle.

 Say the name of each picture. Color the space if the picture name has the short **i** sound. What do you see?

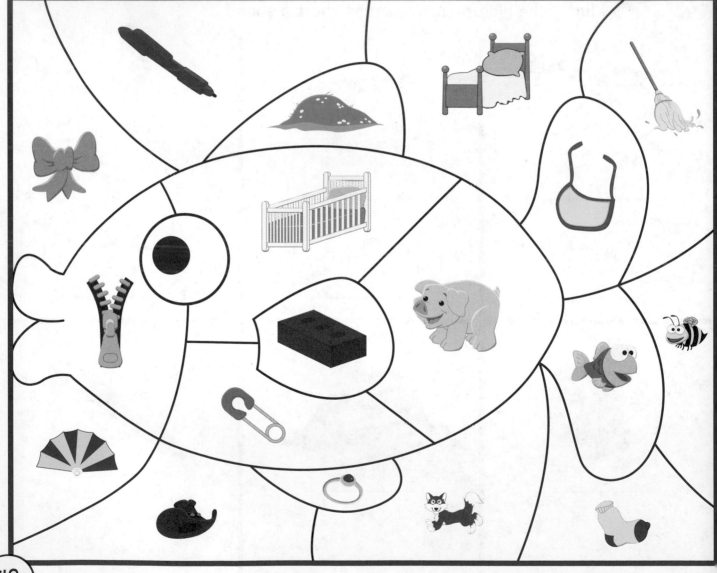

Hip Hip Hooray for School! Learn About Language

Splish, Splash!

Jump in and swim Big Bird!
Swim has the short **i** sound.

 Say the name of each picture. Write **i** on the line if the picture name has the short **i** sound.

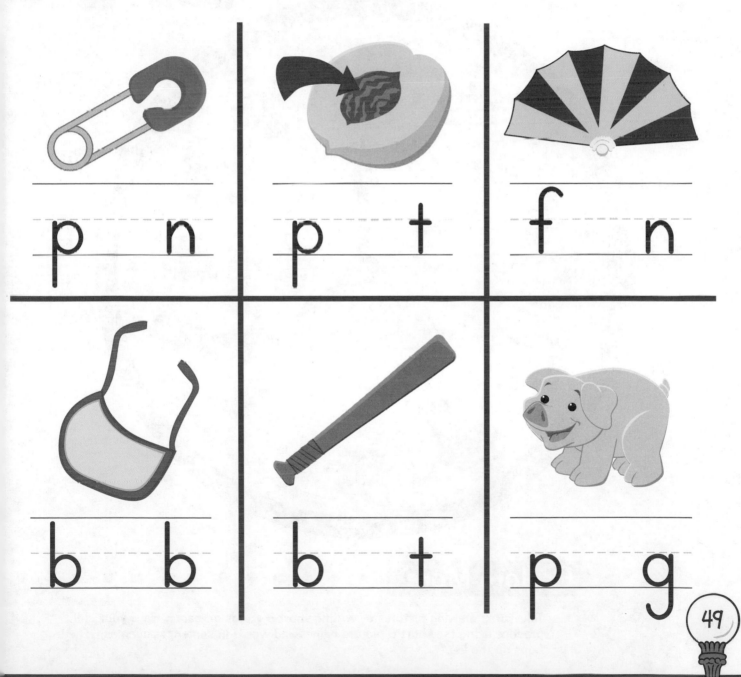

p ___ n	p ___ t	f ___ n
b ___ b	b ___ t	p ___ g

Tick-Tock

Big Bird's clock goes tick-tock.
Clock has the short o sound in the middle.

 Say the name of each picture on the clock.

 Circle each picture that has the short o sound in its name.

Explore More

Take turns drawing pictures or writing short o words on paper. Have your child practice using the short o picture names and words in sentences such as, "The frog hops on the log."

(50)

 **SESAME STREET** Hip Hip Hooray for School! Learn About Language

Hop On!

Big Bird hops on and on.
Hop has the short **o** sound in the middle.

  Say the name of each picture. Write **o** on the line if the picture name has the short **o** sound.

O ___

_ _ _ _ _

_ _ _ _ _

_ _ _ _ _

_ _ _ _ _

_ _ _ _ _

Hip Hip Hooray for School! Learn About Language

Rub-a-Dub-Dub

Big Bird scrubs in the tub.
Tub has the short **u** sound in the middle.

 Say the name of each picture on the tub. Circle each
picture that has the short **u** sound in its name.

Hip Hip Hooray for School! Learn About Language

Munch, munch, munch.
Big Bird is ready for lunch.
Lunch has the short **u** sound in the middle.

 Say the name of each picture and the letter sound you hear in the middle. Write **u** on the line if the picture name has the short **u** sound.

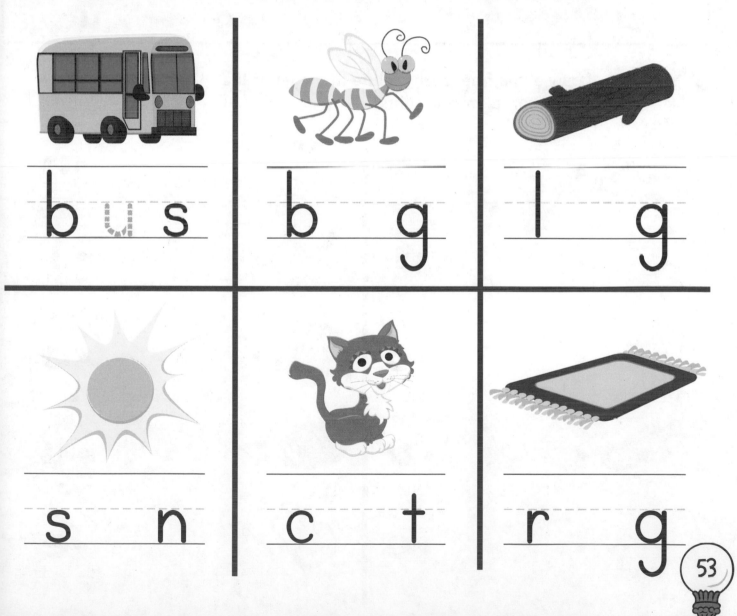

b u s   b ___ g   l ___ g

s ___ n   c ___ t   r ___ g

53

Time to Review

Big Bird has so much fun learning about
the short **a**, **e**, **i**, **o**, and **u** sounds!

 Say the name of each picture.

a **e** **i** **o** **u**

 Draw a line from each picture to the letter that
stands for its middle sound.

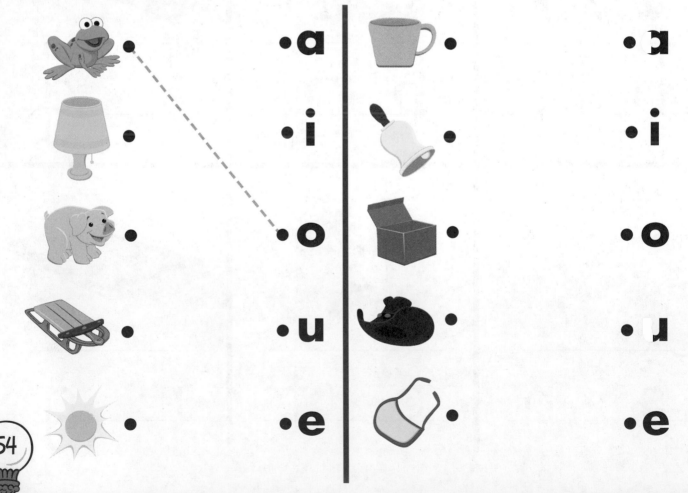

54

SESAME STREET   Hip Hip Hooray for School! Learn About Language

Big Bird knows which sound is
in the middle of his name.

 Say the name of each picture. Circle the
sound you hear in the middle of its name.

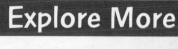

a e i o u

a e i o u

a e i o u

a e i o u

a e i o u

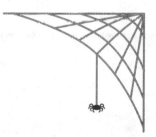

a e i o u

Explore More

Have fun making word webs. Write the letter **a** in the middle of a piece of paper and
draw a circle around it. Then draw six lines, like spokes, coming out from the center
of the circle. Help your child think of words she knows that have the short sound of
a in the middle. Write one word at the end of each line. Or have your child draw
pictures instead of writing the words. Then repeat the activity using the letters **e**, **i**,
o, and **u**.

55

Better Together

Big Bird and his friends have fun making words together.

   Say the sound of each letter. Blend the sounds of the letters together as you say each word. Color the picture that shows the word.

bat

ham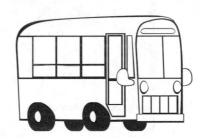

pig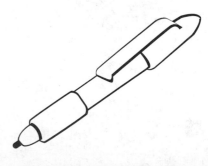

lid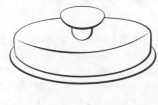

SESAME STREET Hip Hip Hooray for School! Learn About Language

Blend with a Friend

Big Bird and Elmo blend letter sounds into words.

Say the sound of each letter. Blend the sounds of the letters together as you say each word. Then write the word under the picture it names.

bus

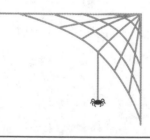

net

dog

web

pot

rug

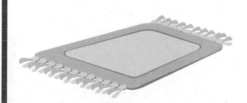

57

Hot Pot

Rhyming words sound the same.
Granny Bird's pot is very hot.
Pot and **hot** rhyme because they
sound the same at the end.

  Say the name of the pictures in each picture pair.
Color the picture pairs if their names rhyme.

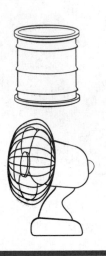  

  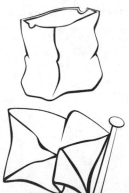

58

Explore More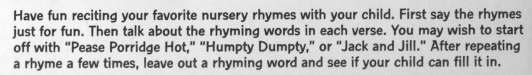

Have fun reciting your favorite nursery rhymes with your child. First say the rhymes
just for fun. Then talk about the rhyming words in each verse. You may wish to start
off with "Pease Porridge Hot," "Humpty Dumpty," or "Jack and Jill." After repeating
a rhyme a few times, leave out a rhyming word and see if your child can fill it in.

Move It!

Rhyming words sound the same. Big Bird will put the fan in the moving van. **Fan** and **van** rhyme because they sound the same at the end.

   Say the name of the pictures in each row. Circle the pictures whose names rhyme. Then draw a picture to show a new rhyming word.

  Say the name of the pictures in each row. Circle the pictures whose names rhyme. Then write a new rhyming word.

It's Raining, It's Pouring

Big Bird can't play his game in the rain.
Play, **game**, and **rain** all have the long **a** sound.

 Say the name of the pictures.

 Circle the picture in each row with the long **a** sound. Then draw a picture of something whose name has the long **a** sound.

 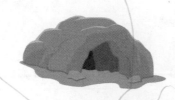 

hat   **rock**   **rake**

hay   **ham**   **jump**

  Say the names of the pictures. Circle the picture in each row with the long **a** sound. Then trace the long **a** word.

cave

sail

For Sale

Big Bird got a pretty pink rake at the yard sale.
Rake and **sale** both have the long **a** sound.

  Say the name of each picture. Help Big Bird get home from the sale by connecting pictures whose names have the long **a** sound.

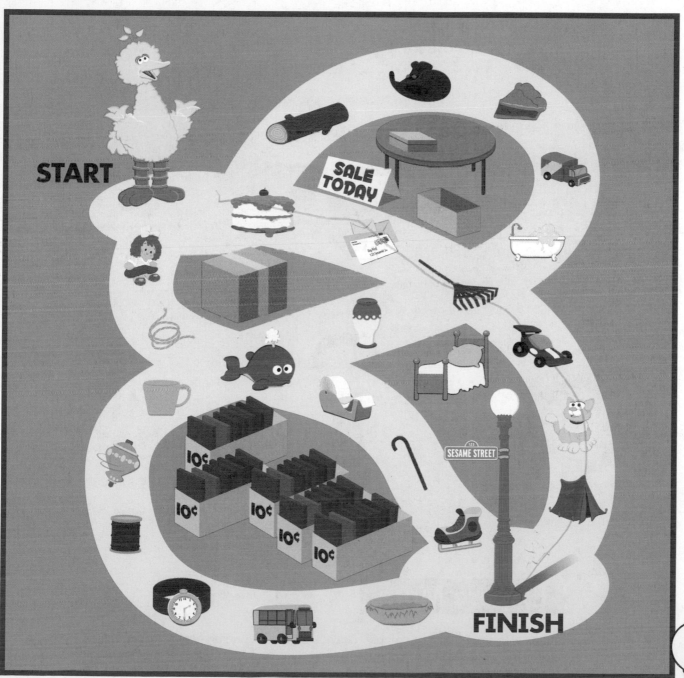

SESAME STREET

Good Night, Sleep Tight

YAWN!

It's **time** for bed Big Bird. Good night!
Time and **night** have the long **i** sound.

 Say the name of each picture. Circle each picture that has the long **i** sound in its name.

Explore More

Make an "I Spy" pie. Draw a large circle on a sheet of paper and add lines to make 4 or 6 slices. Encourage your child to find things whose names have the long **i** sound. Draw the objects and write the words to fill all the pie pieces.

62

Let's Go Fly a Kite

Telly will tie the string so Big Bird's kite flies high.
Tie, kite, and **high** all have the long **i** sound.

   Say the name of each picture. Color the kite if the picture name has the long **i** sound. Then trace the long **i** words.

hive   bike   cake

pie   light   leg

Row Your Boat

Big Bird's boat has a hole. He will row quickly. **Boat, hole,** and **row** all have the long **o** sound.

   Say the name of each picture. Circle the picture in each row with the long **o** sound. Then trace the long **o** word.

cone

soap

bow

   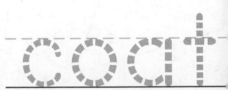

coat

rope

Home Sweet Home

This road will take Big Bird home!
Road and **home** have the long **o** sound.

 Play tic-tac-toe. Say the name of each picture. Draw an **O** around three pictures in a row whose names have the long **o** sound.

65

June and July

Big Bird is buying a blue bathing suit to wear in June and July. **Blue**, **suit**, and **June** have the long **u** sound.

  Say the name of each picture. Circle each picture that has the long **u** sound in its name.

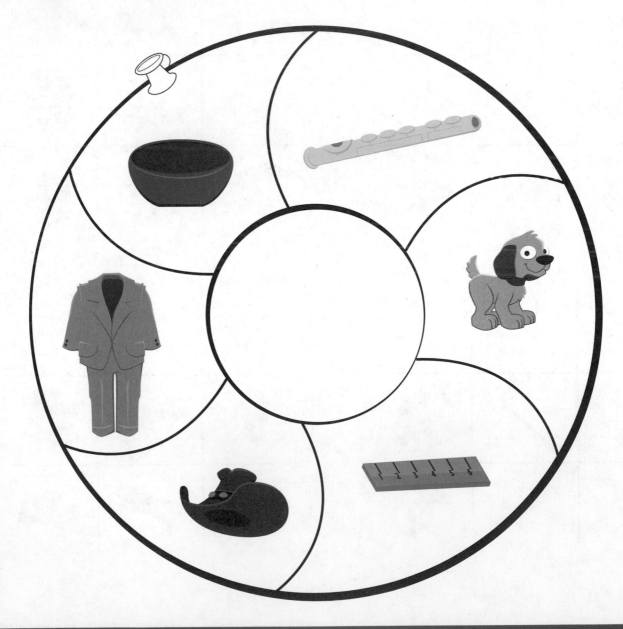

Hip Hip Hooray for School! Learn About Language

A Happy Tune

Big Bird plays the flute in his blue suit.
Flute, **blue**, and **suit** all have the long **u** sound.

 Say the name of each picture. Color the picture if its name has the long **u** sound. Then trace the long **u** words.

June

glue

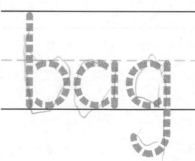

bag

suit

sail

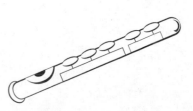

flute

Hip Hip Hooray for School! Learn About Language SESAME STREET

Feel the Beat

Move your feet to the beat.
Feet and **beat** have the long **e** sound.

  Say the name of each picture.
Color each picture that has the long **e** sound in its name.

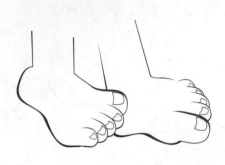  

Explore More ■ ◆ ● ■ ◆ ● ■ ◆ ● ■ ◆ ●

Talk with your child about all of the things your feet can do. Then trace your child's feet on a piece of paper. Tell your child to decorate his "feet" by drawing or writing long **e** words on the footprints.

The Green Team

Big Bird is on the green team.
Green and **team** both have
the long **e** sound.

   Say the name of each picture. Circle the picture in each row with the long **e** sound. Then trace the long **e** word.

meat

  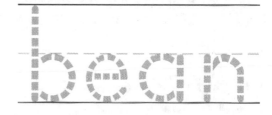

bean

tree

peel

69

 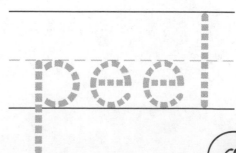

a e i o u

Big Bird knows all of the long **a**, **e**, **i**, **o**, and **u** sounds!

  Say the name of each picture.

a   **e**   **i**   **o**   **u**

 Draw a line from each picture to the letter that stands for its middle sound. Look at the pictures in the box if you need help.

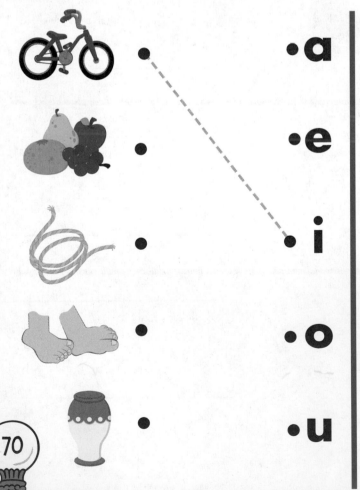

 • **a**

 • **e**

 • **i**

 • **o**

 • **u**

 •**a**

 •**e**

•**i**

 •**o**

 •**u**

70

Time to Review

Big Bird loves learning about vowel sounds!

   Say the name of each picture. Circle the sound you hear in the middle of its name.

a e i o u	a e i o u	a e i o u
		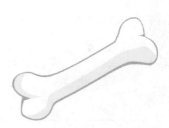
a e i o u	a e i o u	a e i o u

Hip Hip Hooray for School! Learn About Language

SESAME STREET

Big Bird and Herry Monster love making long vowel words, like **bike** and **ride**.

 Say the name of each picture. Write the correct long vowel letter to finish each word.

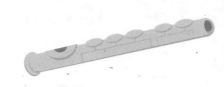

bike   c o at   flu te

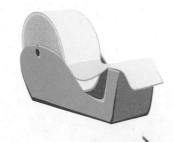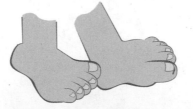

t a pe   f e et   c o ne

r o be   l i me

k i te   r a ke

Explore More

Help your child make a list of things she likes to do by herself or with you. For example, ride a bike or sail a boat. Read the list together and underline any words that have the sound of long **a**, **e**, **i**, **o**, or **u**.

73

Hip Hip Hooray for School! Learn About Language

SESAME STREET

Dive in the Hive

Rhyming words sound the same. Big Bird sees five bees dive in the hive. **Five**, **dive**, and **hive** rhyme because they sound the same at the end.

 Say the names of the pictures in each hive. Color the hive if the picture names rhyme.

74

Make and Take

What will Big Bird make to take to the lake?
Make, take, and **lake** rhyme.

  Say the name of each picture. In each row, circle the pictures whose names rhyme.

 Then draw a new picture to show another rhyming word.

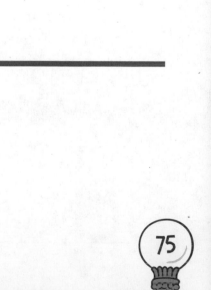

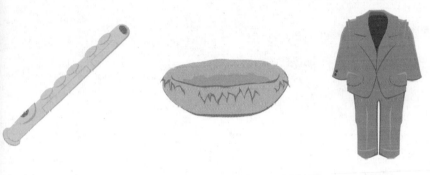

Hip Hip Hooray for School! Learn About Language

SESAME STREET

Fill'er Up

Big Bird and Elmo fill up the cups.

  Say the name of each picture. Write the missing vowel and say the letter. Then read each short vowel word.

a e i o u

c u p   p g   s u n

 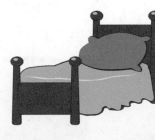 

d g   b e d   c t

76

SESAME STREET   Hip Hip Hooray for School! Learn About Language

Beep! Beep!

Beep! Beep!
Here comes Big Bird's jeep!

 Say the name of each picture. Trace the letters. Then read each word.

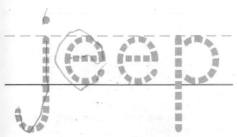

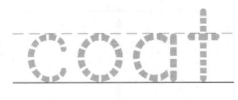

A Bat, On Base

Big Bird is at bat to see if he can get on base.
Bat has a short **a** sound. **Base** has a long **a** sound.

   Say the words in each box. Circle the word with the short **a** or long **a** sound. Then draw a picture to show the word.

soap cat tub	net sun hat
cane kite feet	rake bike flute

 Hip Hip Hooray for School! Learn About Language

Short or Long Vowel Sound?

Radar has a short **e** word and
Big Bird has a long **e** word.

  Say the name of each picture.

  Color the picture **red** if you hear a short vowel sound.
Color the picture **green** if you hear a long vowel sound.

79

Big Bird spies some letters that make a
special message for Granny Bird.

  Trace each letter. Then, find and circle
those letters hidden in the picture.

I love you.

80

KNOW YOUR NUMBERS

Numbers, numbers everywhere!
1-2-3, get ready to count,
trace, and write numbers with
all the Sesame Street friends!

LEARN TO:

- Count from 1-10
- Follow number order
- Trace & write numbers 1-10

Family Activities

Counting Collage
Using several pieces of blank paper, write a number in pencil on each one. Encourage your child to trace over the number with her finger or a marker and add her own drawings to show the number. For example, if the number is **2**, she might choose to draw **2** stars, **2** smile faces, **2** circles, or **2** hearts.

Nibbling On Nine
Help your child make a healthy snack mix while learning about counting. Choose several small food items (like pretzels, crackers, cereal pieces, or low-fat granola pieces). Have him count out **9** of each item and place them in a bag. Shake the bag to mix the snack and enjoy

Ten Terrific Toes
How many terrific things can you do with your toes while counting to **10**? Help your child count her toes to **10** and then back down to **1** again. Encourage her to wiggle or tap her toes **10** times each, or dance while you help her count to **10**. Can she tip toe **10** tiny steps, too? Now see how many things she can do with her **10** fingers while counting to **10**!

Adding Eggs
Find two plastic eggs that snap together or two clean empty containers (like a sour cream or butter container). Choose a small object like pretzel sticks, crackers, cereal pieces, or raisins and place some of the items inside each plastic container. Have your child count how many items are in the first container and how many are in the second container, then add them together to find the total. Allow your child to eat some of the snacks, then count and add again.

Bert's Missing Number Game
Bert loves collecting bottle caps! Help your child collect **10** bottle caps and write the numbers **1** to **10**, one on each cap. Encourage your child to lay the caps out on the floor or table in the correct number sequence. Then have him hide his eyes (or turn around) and you take one of the caps away, closing up the space where the number was on the table. Have your child tell you which number is missing! Switch roles and play again.

Let's Write Numbers!
Encourage your child to write with different tools to practice recognizing the lines and shapes that make up the numbers. You can use markers, crayons, colored pens, pencils, watercolor paints, and different kinds or shapes of paper. For a different kind of number fun, allow your child to use a bar of soap to write the numbers on dark colored construction paper. Encourage your child to look for numbers around the house and record them on the dark paper with the soap.

Color the balloons with numbers **red**. Color the balloons without numbers **blue**.

83

Hip Hip Hooray for School! Know Your Numbers   SESAME STREET 123

1 one

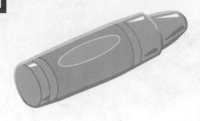

 Trace the number **1**. Then write some of your own.

 Count **1** doll. Then color the doll.

Explore More

Encourage your child to practice counting fun, healthy foods like raisins, carrots, or dry cereal. Extend the learning by helping him place the items into groups, such as 2 apples, 5 carrots, etc.

84

Circle the flowerpots that have **1** flower. Then color them.

Look at the pictures. Circle the picture that shows **1**.

2

2 two

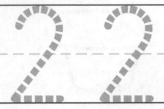  Trace the number **2**. Then write some of your own.

2 2

 Count **2** tutus. Then color them.

86

Color the **2** eyes and **2** ears on each of the friends.

 Draw **2** eyes and **2** ears to make a new friend.

Explore More ■ ◆ ● ■ ◆ ● ■ ◆ ● ■ ◆ ●

Help your child count the things in one room of your home. Demonstrate by looking around the living room and counting: 1 sofa, 3 chairs, 2 tables, and 1 rug. Try counting things in other rooms too!

 SESAME STREET

3

3 three

  Trace the number **3**. Then write some of your own.

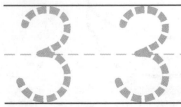

  Count **3** tricycles. Then color them.

Circle the groups that show **3**.

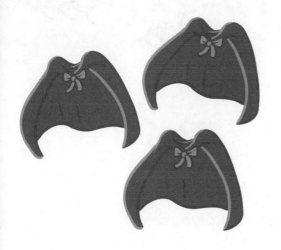

 Color **3** things in each row.

 89

4 four

  Trace the number **4**. Then write some of your own.

  Count **4** garbage cans. Then color them.

Trace 1 more barrel to make **4** all together. Then color it.

 Draw a line from each number to the group that shows how many.

1

2

3

4

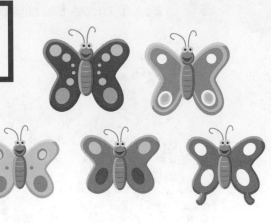

5 five

 Trace the number **5**. Then write some of your own.

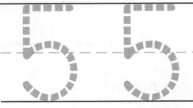

 Count **5** flowers. Then color them.

 92

Circle **5** dresses for Prairie Dawn to wear.

 Circle the number to show how many in each row.

   **5**   **3**   **1**

   **2**   **1**   **4**

   **3**   **5**   **2**

6 six

 Trace the number **6**. Then write some of your own.

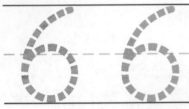

 Cookie Monster likes lots of milk with his cookies!
Count **6** glasses of milk. Then color them.

94

Rosita loves to bake muffins.
Draw **6** chocolate chips on the muffin.

Draw an **X** on **6** objects in each group.

95

SESAME STREET

7

7 seven

Trace the number **7**. Then write some of your own.

Count **7** nests. Then color them.

Count and color **7** bats.

Look at the number at the beginning of each row.
Then draw an **X** on that number of objects.

5

6

7

Explore More ■ ◆ ● ◆ ■ ◆ ● ◆ ■

Each day on Sesame Street, the Count picks a number of the day. Encourage your child to pick a number of the day at home, too! If your child picks **7** as the number of the day, help her find and count things in groups of **7** all day.

97

8 eight

 Trace the number **8**. Then write some of your own.

8 8

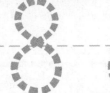 Count **8** dog bones. Then color them.

Trace the door on **8** of the doghouses.

Circle the group with **8**.

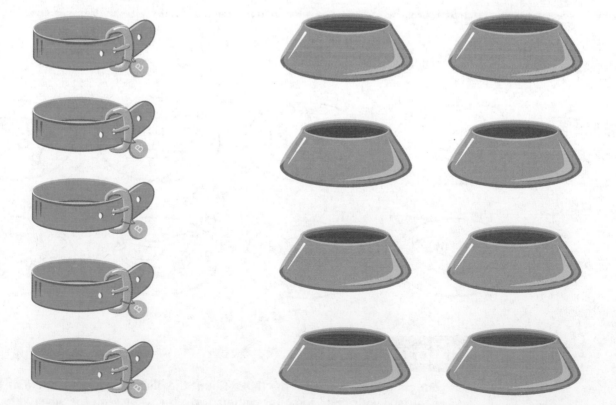

Hip Hip Hooray for School! Know Your Numbers

123 **SESAME STREET**

9 nine

 Trace the number **9**. Then write some of your own.

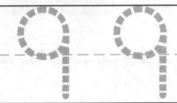

 Count **9** dishes. Then color them.

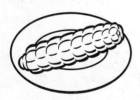    

Explore More ■ ◆ ● ■ ◆ ● ■ ◆ ●

100

Ask your child to help you set the table. Count the dishes as you put them on the tab
and encourage your child to count with you. Do the same with the silverware, glasses
and cups.

 SESAME STREET Hip Hip Hooray for School! Know Your Numbers

Draw more teacups to make **9** all together.

 Circle the group with **9**.

10 ten

 Trace the number **10**. Then write some of your own.

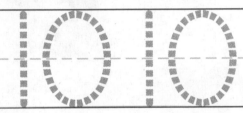

Count **10** skateboards. Then color them.

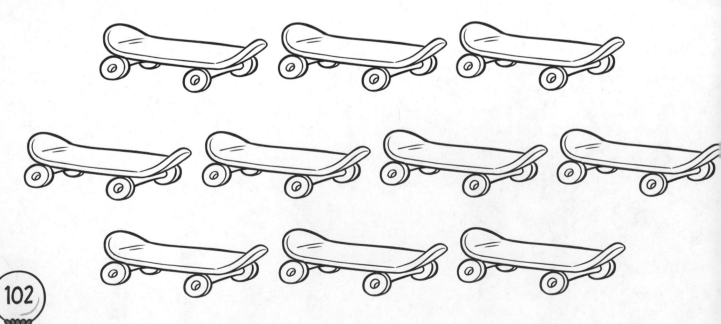

Draw more bubbles to make **10** all together.

 Draw an **X** on **10** things in each group.

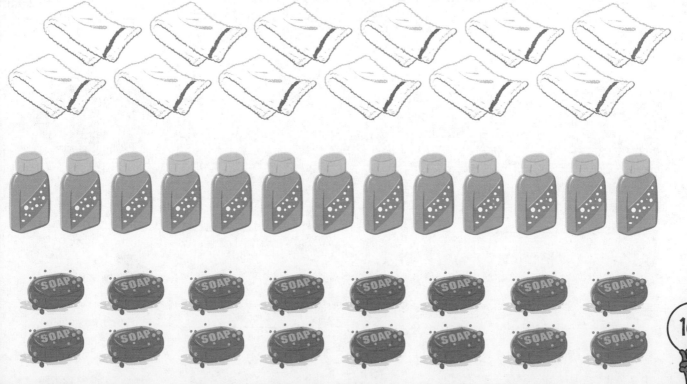

How many do you see?

Count each fruit. Then write how many.

How many do you see?

 **Count each animal. Then write how many.**

Draw a line to connect the **orange** dots from **1** to **10**.
Draw a line to connect the **green** dots from **1** to **10**.

Color the picture.

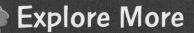
Explore More

Go on a number hunt with your child. Look for things in your home like telephone
books, and computers that have the numbers **1** to **10** on them. Encourage your chi
to point to and say each number.

Learn About
MATH

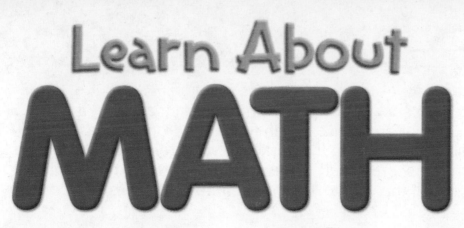

One Ernie plus one Bert equals two silly friends! Are you ready to count, add, subtract, and learn about math with them?

LEARN TO:
- Count and skip count
- Recognize numbers and number order
- Identify shapes and the size of groups
- Add and subtract

Skip Counting Basketball
Find a soft ball or rolled up socks, an empty laundry basket, a sheet of paper, and a pencil to keep score. Choose a spot about five or ten feet away from the basket and take turns trying to shoot the ball and make it in the basket. If you or your child scores a basket, write the number **2** on the score sheet; if you score again, write the number **4** next to the **2**. See if she can make it all the way to **10** and then **20** baskets as you count by **2**s!

Shape Drawings
Find some blank sheets of paper and different colored crayons or markers for this shape game. Show your child how to make shape pictures by drawing a shape on the sheet of paper. Be sure to explain the name of the shape and its characteristics (for example, a square has four sides that are all the same length). Then add lines, other shapes and various details to the shape to make a picture! For example, you may want to add a triangle roof, a door, and some windows to the square to make a house. Try other shapes, too!

Counting Backwards
Turn clean-up time or dressing time into a backwards-counting game. Help your child get ready for a task by counting down from **10** or **20**. You might say something like, "When I count from **10** to **1**, it will be time to start cleaning up your toys." Then count down with your child and help her clean up. Try this with other tasks too, like getting dressed, getting out of the bath, or waiting for her turn at something.

Who Has More?
Hide both hands behind your back and encourage your child to do the same. Explain that when you count to **3**, you and your child will place both of your hands in view with a certain number of fingers held up (your child can choose how many to show). Then he must count, think, and decide who is showing **more** fingers.

Two Much Fun!
Find some blank pieces of paper and crayons or markers for this silly bug adding game. Draw a simple circle for a bug's body. Tell a story to prompt her to add body parts to the bug and add up the parts. For example, you might say, "**2** legs plus **2** more legs equals how many legs all together?" Encourage her to draw the legs and then count them to find the answer. Continue this game by adding eyes, antennae, or bug friends, too.

Subtracting Snack
Place a snack on a plate for your child and ask him to count how many items there are all together. You may want to choose a snack like small finger sandwiches, raw green beans, crackers, banana slices, or cheese chunks. Encourage him to eat **1** of the snacks and count again to see how many are left. Talk about it together by saying something like, "That's right, you had **6** banana slices and you ate **1**, so now there are **5** left."

108

It's a Match!

Sometimes things look alike. They are the **same!**

 Draw a line to match the objects that are the **same.**

Sometimes things belong together even though they are **different.**

 Draw a line to match the things that belong together.

(109)

Colorful Sorting

Some things are almost the same but have a **different** color. Ernie wants to sort his fish by color.

 Draw a line from each yellow fish to the fish tank on the yellow mat.
Draw a line from each pink fish to the tank on the pink mat.

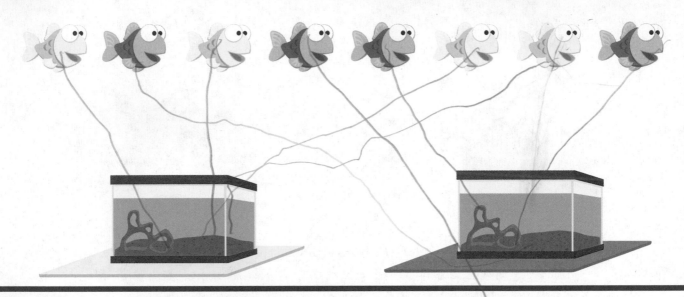

Next, Ernie wants to sort Bert's bottle cap collection by color.

 Draw a line from each bottle cap to the **same** color bottle.

110

Clean Up Time!

Some things are **different** sizes. Elmo has big toys and little toys. He wants to sort all his toys by size and put them away.

 Draw a line from each **big** toy to the **big** box.
Draw a line from each **small** toy to the **small** box.

Explore More

Sorting is a good way to help your child learn about how things are **different** and how they are the **same**. Fill a big box or laundry basket with items and encourage your child to sort the items in **different** ways: by color; by size; by shape; by which family member it belongs to; or by category (for example: toys with toys, books with books, clothes with clothes). Your child can draw pictures of big things, red things, or square things, too.

111

Hip Hip Hooray for School! Learn About Math   SESAME STREET

Big, Bigger, Biggest

These friends are different sizes! Ernie is **big**. Cookie Monster is **bigger**. Big Bird is the **biggest** of all.

 Color the object in each row that is the **biggest**.

  Draw and color a picture of something that is **bigger** than you.

Small, Smaller, Smallest

Baby Bear is **small**. Elmo is **smaller**.
Natasha is the **smallest**.

 Circle the object in each row that is the **smallest**.

Draw and color a picture of something that is **smaller** than you.

113

The Same Game

Zoe has **2** balls. Elmo has **2** flippers. They both have **2**! They have the same number of things!

  Count the objects in each group. Then draw a line to match the groups that have the **same** number of objects.

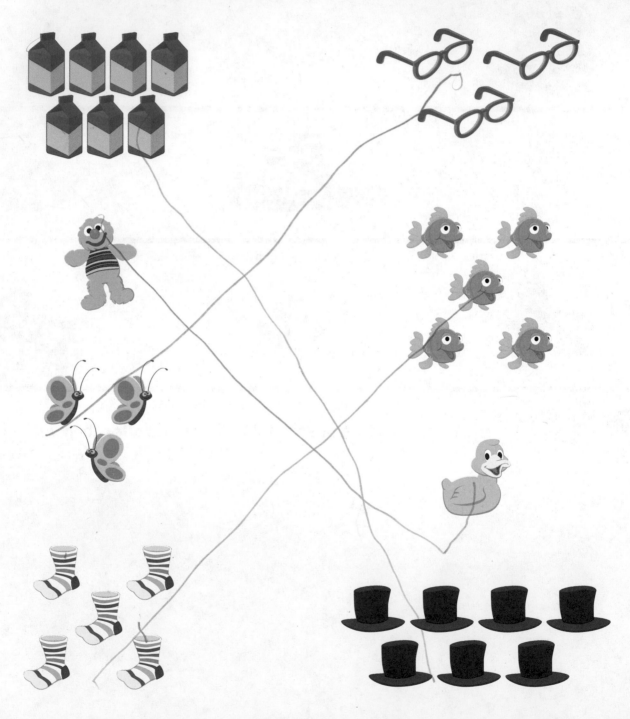

It's All the Same to Me!

Grover has the **same** number of bowls on each tray.

  Count the objects in each group. Then circle the two groups in each row that have the **same** number of objects.

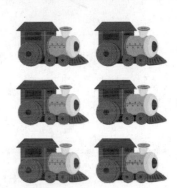

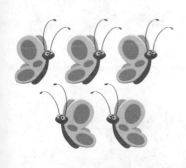

SESAME STREET

Which Has More?

Abby Cadabby is sitting on the pile with **more** pumpkins.

  Count the objects in each group. Then circle the group in each row with **more**.

Explore More

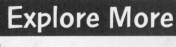

Use snack time as an opportunity to reinforce the concepts of **more**, and the **same**. For example, put some crackers on two plates, and ask your child which one has **more**. Put some apple slices on one plate for her and on another for you; ask her to help you place the **same** number of apples on each plate.

Hip Hip Hooray for School! Learn About Math

Which Has Less?

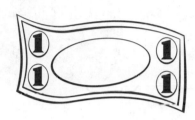

Ernie's blue bottle of bubble bath has **less** bubble bath in it than the other bottle.

  Look at the objects in each group. Then color the group in each row with **less**.

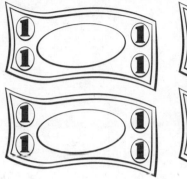 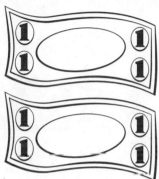

 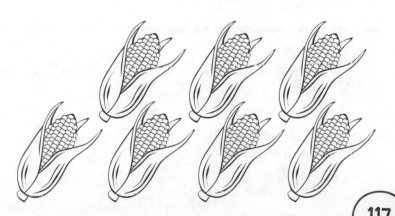

Hip Hip Hooray for School! Learn About Math   SESAME STREET

More or Less

The **green** bowl has **more** fruit than the **red** bowl.
The **red** bowl has **less** fruit than the **green** bowl.

 Draw a picture that shows **more** fruit than the green bowl.

 Draw a picture that shows **less** flowers than the vase.

 Draw and color the **same** number of caterpillars as the first picture.

118

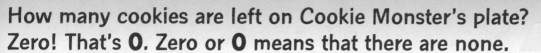

How many cookies are left on Cookie Monster's plate?
Zero! That's **0**. Zero or **0** means that there are none.

 Write a **0** next to each box that has zero objects in it.
Count the other objects and write how many.

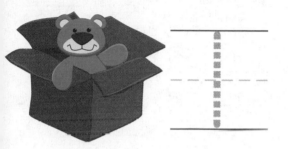 1

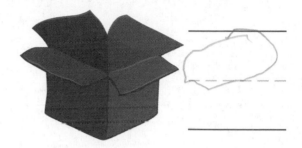

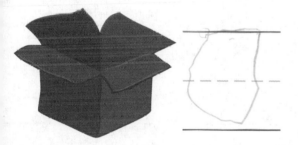

 5

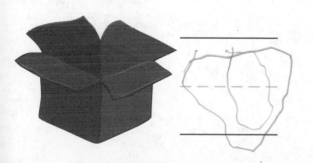

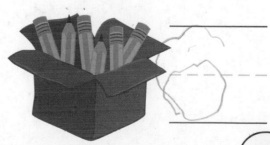

119

Hip Hip Hooray for School! Learn About Math   **SESAME STREET**

 Count the things in each group. Then trace each number to show how many.

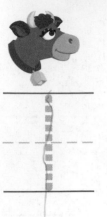

1 2 3 4

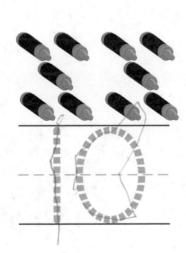

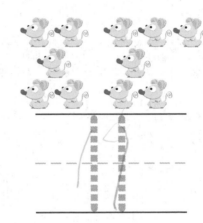

9 10 11 12

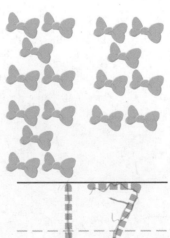

16 17 18

5

6

7

8

13

14

15

19

20

3

121

Hip Hip Hooray for School! Learn About Math   SESAME STREET

Home, Sweet Home

You love to count, too? Wonderful! *Ah, ah, ah!*

 Draw a line to connect the dots from **1–20** to see where the Count is standing.

 Color the picture.

11

10 9   12
         13

6   16

5   17

7   15
  8   14

4   18
3   19

2   1   20

(122)

Explore More

Make a set of number cards with your child, mix them up, and encourage him to put the cards in order from 1-10. See if he can put them in order backwards from 10-1. Make it a countdown race to see how fast he can do it. When he is ready, add the numbers 11-20 to the card set.

Zoe counts 1 doll.

Count the objects in each group. Then draw a line to the number that shows how many.

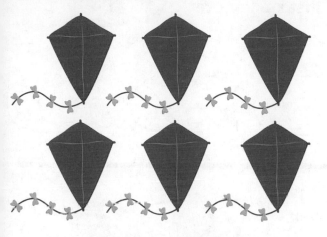

4

6

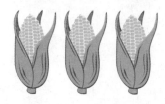

5

3

123

Hip Hip Hooray for School! Learn About Math

SESAME STREET

Keep Counting!

Count Von Count counts **5** batty bats.
Help him count more things!

 Count and color **3** objects from each group.
Draw an **X** on the objects that are left over.

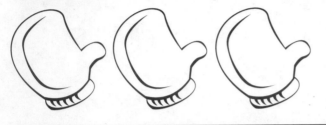

(124)

Hip Hip Hooray for School! Learn About Math

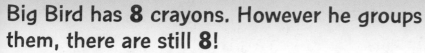

Big Bird has **8** crayons. However he groups them, there are still **8**!

 Count the crayons in each group. Write how many crayons are in each group.

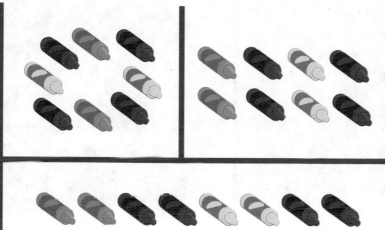

 Draw and color your own group of **8** crayons.

Explore More

Help your child see that **8** is always **8** by practicing with everyday items. Choose items like toy cars or stuffed animals and see how many ways your child can organize and arrange them. You may want to suggest a long single line, a circle arrangement, or two-by-twos. Let your child be creative and see what other ways she can come up with to arrange them. Count again. It's still **8**!

125

Hip Hip Hooray for School! Learn About Math

Bert has **10** bottle caps. Bert wants to count more **things** to **10**.

 Count each group of objects. Draw an **X** on the group that does not show **10**.

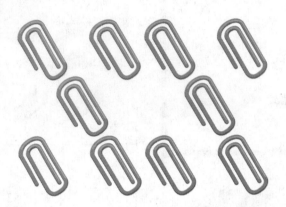

Explore More

You can count to **10**! Have your child trace both hands on a sheet of paper. Together, help your child draw a picture or place a sticker on each finger. Count the pictures when you are done — that's **10**! Help him trace his feet, too!

126

SESAME STREET   Hip Hip Hooray for School! Learn About Math

There are lots of ways to show the number **10**.

 Trace the word ten and the number **10**.
Count the dots and **X**s.

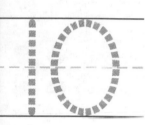

Let's get Ernie's bath ready for him.

 Draw **10** bubbles for Ernie's bath.

Hip Hip Hooray for School! Learn About Math   **SESAME STREET**

Ernie likes to count with Rubber Duckie.
Squeak, squeak!

  Say the numbers from **1–20**.
Write in the missing numbers.

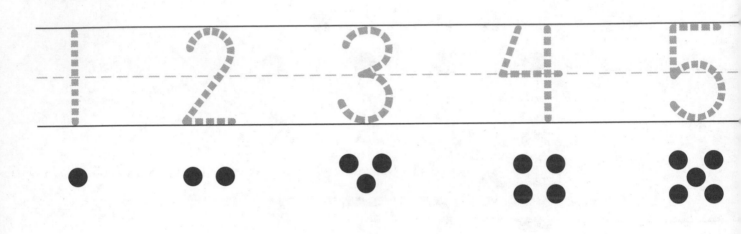

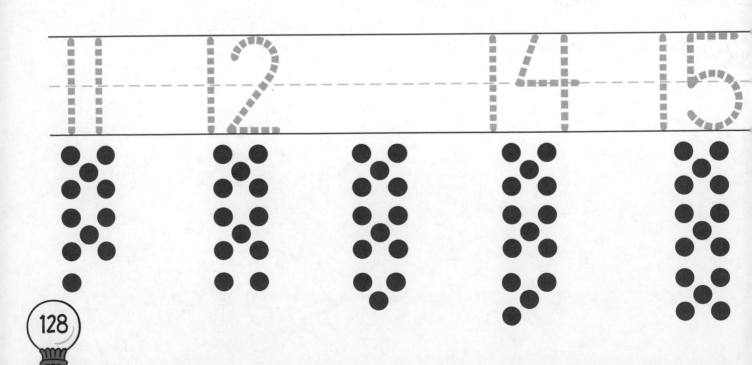

Bert and Bernice keep counting, all the way to **20**.

 Count the dots under each number.
Then, trace the number.

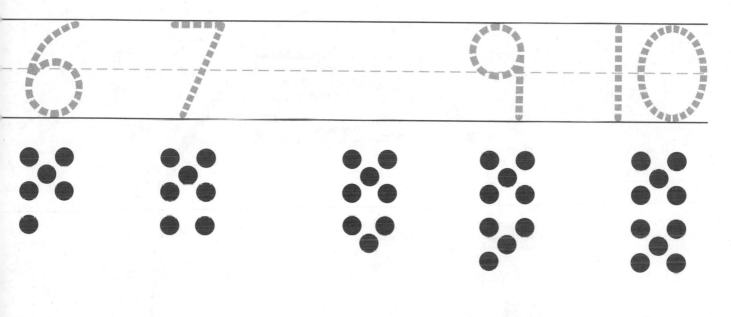

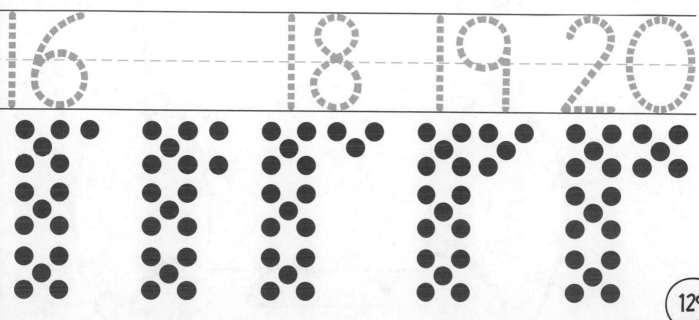

Oscar's worm pal, Slimey, is on his way to the moon. Help count backwards from **10** down to **0** for lift-off.

 Draw a line to connect the dots from **10** down to **0**.

 Say the numbers as you count backwards. Then color the picture.

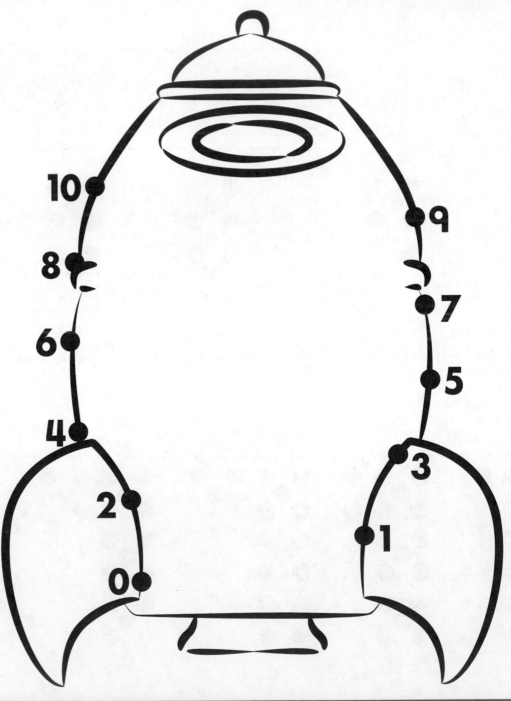

10 9 8 7 6 5 4 3 2 1 0

 130

Happy Birthday, Elmo!

Elmo got a present for his birthday!

 Draw a line to connect the dots backwards from **20** down to **0** to see Elmo's gift.

 Say the numbers as you count backwards. Then color the picture.

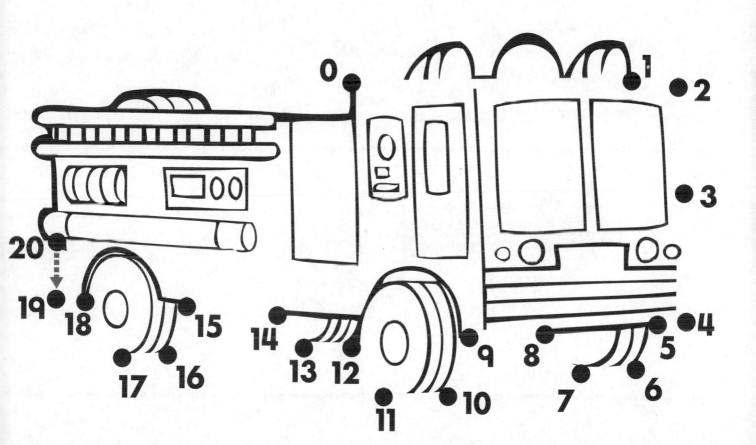

Explore More

Practice counting backwards! Try showing your child how to count backwards until the cookies are done baking, or until someone arrives home, or as she races to get dressed in the morning. Or, draw a number line on the sidewalk with chalk, and have your child jump backwards as she says the numbers from **20** to **0**.

131

Zoe is **first** in line. Rosita is next. Elmo is **last**.

 Circle the friend who is **first** in each row.
Color the friend who is **last** in each row.

 Hip Hip Hooray for School! Learn About Math

Grover is **1st**. Rosita is **2nd**. Ernie is **3rd**.

 Trace over the numbers on each car of the roller coaster. Then draw yourself in the **3rd** car!

 Use the color key below to color the cars.

1st   **2nd**   **3rd**

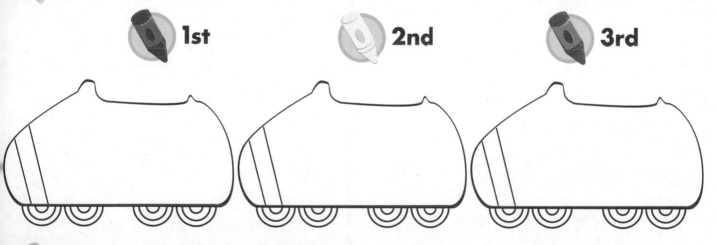

Explore More ◾ ◆ ● ◾ ◆ ● ◾ ◆ ● ◾ ◆ ● ◾ ◆

Have your child practice **1st**, **2nd**, and **3rd** with stuffed animals or other friends. Encourage him to line up 3 stuffed animals in a row. Then you may ask a question like, "Who is **1st**?" Or, give your child clues and encourage him to put the animals in the order that you suggest. For example, you might say, "Please place the green animal **1st**, the yellow animal **2nd**, and the brown animal **3rd**."

133

Hip Hip Hooray for School! Learn About Math   SESAME STREET

Rosita is learning all about shapes.

 Trace each shape. Then draw some of your own.

circle

oval

 Trace each shape. Count the sides on each shape as you trace.

rhombus

rectangle

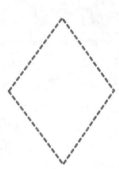

square

pentagon

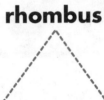

hexagon

triangle

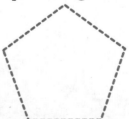

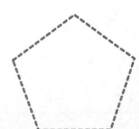

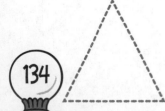

SESAME STREET   Hip Hip Hooray for School! Learn About Math

Draw a line to help Zoe follow the path of   to get to Elmo.

START

FINISH

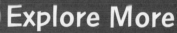

Explore More

Shapes can be found everywhere! Help your child find shapes in and around the neighborhood. Look for shapes on signs, on stores, on buildings, in the grocery store, in nature, and in your home. Make today a Circle Day, and see how many different circles you can find or draw pictures made with circles. Try another shape tomorrow.

135

Porridge, Please!

Baby Bear and Mama Bear are ready for breakfast.
Each bear needs one bowl of porridge and one glass
of juice.

 Draw **1** bowl of porridge and **1** glass of juice for each bear.

Explore More ■ ◆ ● ■ ◆ ● ■ ◆ ● ◆ ●

One-to-one correspondence is an important math skill, and setting the table is an easy
way to demonstrate this concept. Ask your child to count how many people will be
sitting at the table. Then have her get out that same number of plates, spoons, and
so on. You can offer a model for one place setting to help reinforce patterning (spoon
goes on the right, cup goes above the plate, napkin goes on the left). Then let your
child repeat the pattern with each place setting.

SESAME STREET   Hip Hip Hooray for School! Learn About Math

Ready to Ride

Elmo wants to go for a bike ride with his friends.

 Draw a line from each friend to a bike.

 Count and write the number of friends. | Count and write the number of bikes.

_____   _____

- - - - - - - - -   - - - - - - - - -

_____   _____

137

Two-by-Two

It's fun to count by 2s! Ah, ah, ah!

  Count the lightning bolts. Trace the number that shows how many.

 When you're finished, say the numbers out loud. You're counting by 2s!

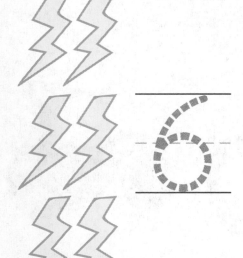

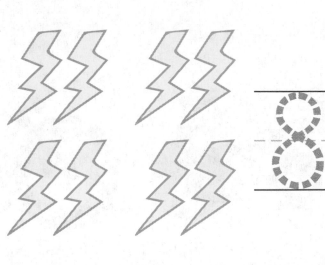

 138

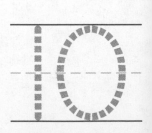

Oscar is counting stinky socks by **2**s.

Count each group of objects.
Write the number to show how many.

When you're finished, say
the numbers out loud.

_____

_ _ _ _ _ _ _ _ _ _ _

_____

_____

_ _ _ _ _ _ _ _ _ _ _

_____

_____

_ _ _ _ _ _ _ _ _ _ _

_____

_____

_ _ _ _ _ _ _ _ _ _ _

_____

_____

_ _ _ _ _ _ _ _ _ _ _

_____

You are counting by 2s!

Explore More

Get some colored chalk and make a hop scotch game outside on the sidewalk
or driveway. Instead of numbering the squares the typical way from **1-10**, write
the numbers by **2**s instead: **2, 4, 6, 8, 10** and so on, up to **20**. Your child can
count by **2**s as he hops.

The Whole Story

Cookie Monster sees cake on the table. He is not eating the **whole** thing, just **part** of it!

 Draw a line to match the **part** to the **whole** object.

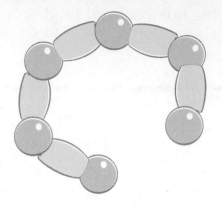

140

SESAME STREET   Hip Hip Hooray for School! Learn About Math

Big Bird has some delicious muffins. That's too many for Big Bird to eat, so he will share them with friends.

Draw a line from each muffin to a friend so they each have the same number of muffins.

Then write how many muffins there are for each friend.

Explore More

Share a snack with your child. Give her some crackers (maybe **6**) and **2** plates (**1** for you and **1** for your child). Ask her to separate the crackers so you each get the same amount. Try the same thing with **3** or **4** people (or stuffed animals), so there are more friends sharing the same number of crackers.

141

How Many All Together?

Grover has **2** yellow balls and **2** red balls.
That's **4** balls all together! Whew!

  Count the objects in each row. Then circle the group at the end that shows how many all together.

 **+**  **=**

1   **1**

 +  **=**

1   **3**

 **+** **=**

2   **1**

 **+**  **=**

3   **2**

Grover is trying to collect all of his sheep.

 Count the sheep along the path. Add the sheep to see how many there are all together.

 Then draw a line on the path that leads to the correct number of sheep all together.

143

Elmo thinks Dorothy is lonely. She needs a fishy friend.

 Count the fish in each bowl and trace each number below.

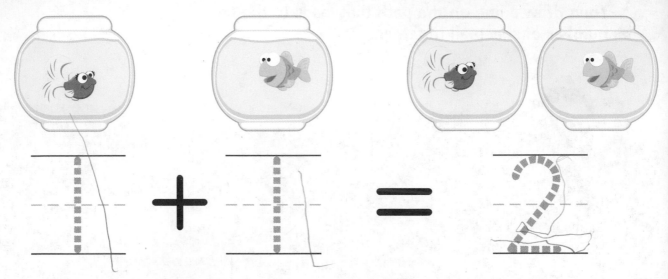

1 Dorothy plus 1 more fish friend — that's 2 fish all together!

Now Elmo needs to feed his fishy friends—1 food flake for each friend.

 Count the flakes in each group and trace each number below.

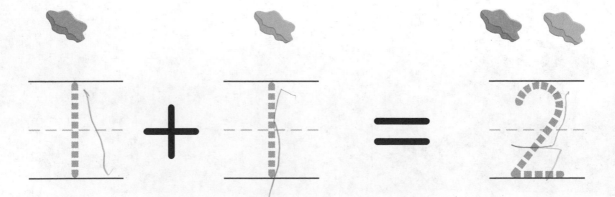

1 food flake for Dorothy plus 1 food flake for her friend — that's 2 food flakes all together!

144

Add It Up

Count the objects in each group. Draw a picture at the end that shows how many all together.

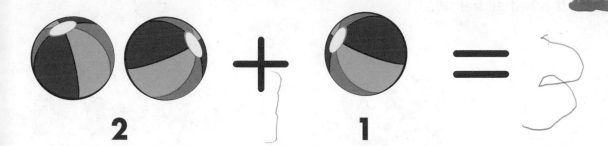

2 + **1** = 3

1 + **4** = 5

3 + **2** = 5

1 + **3** = 4

Hip Hip Hooray for School! Learn About Math   SESAME STREET

Friends for Bernice

Bert likes to bird-watch with his friend, Bernice. Here come some of Bernice's friends!

  Count the birds in each group and write each number below.

1 Bernice + **2** friends = **3** pigeons all together.

   Count Bernice and all her friends. Write the number to show how many birds there are all together.

1   **4**

(146) **1** Bernice and **4** bird friends — that's **5** pigeons all together. You are adding!

Beach Fun

There are so many ways to play at the beach!

   Color the first group of objects. Color **1** more. Count and write how many all together.

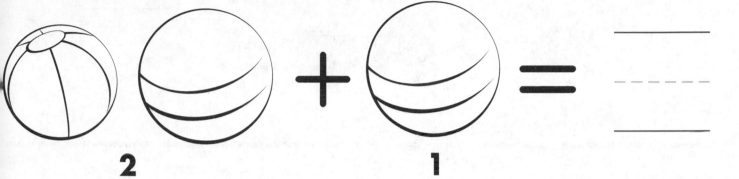

2   1

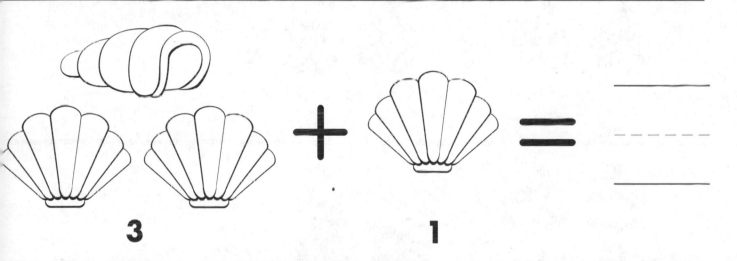

3   1

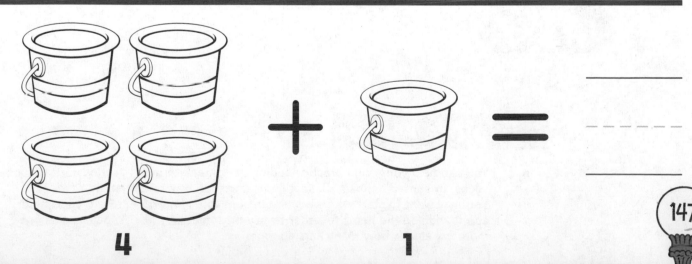

4   1

Hip Hip Hooray for School! Learn About Math

SESAME STREET

Eating and Adding

The Two-Headed Monster wants to find out how many apples he has all together. Help him add!

 Count to add the apples together and write how many all together.

1 + 2 = _____

2 + 2 = _____

4 + 2 = _____

Explore More ▪ ◆ ▪ ◆ ● ▪ ◆ ● ▪ ● ▪ ◆ ●

You can help your child practice adding at home with items like toy cars, crayons, socks, or stuffed animals. Collect items and then separate them into two piles. You may want to start with simple equations like 1+1, or 2+2. Help your child count and add the items together by saying something like, "One car plus one more car equals how many cars all together?"

148

Bert and Ernie are adding things at the park.

Color the first group of objects. Color **2** more. Count and write how many all together.

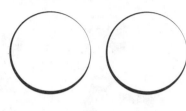

○ **+** ○ ○ **=** ___

1   **2**

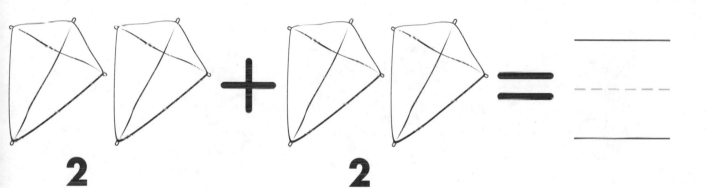

2   **2**

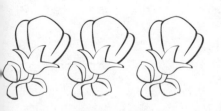 **+**  **=** ___

3   **2**

149

Fly Away, Fairies!

Abby Cadabby is having fun with some friendly fairies. But wait, some are flying away!

 Count the fairies. Then draw an **X** on the ones that are flying away. Write how many are left.

4   **—**   **2**   **=**   _____

4   **—**   **3**   **=**   _____

5   **—**   **2**   **=**   _____

Cookie Monster sees a plate with **2** cookies.
He wants to eat **1** cookie.

 Count the cookies on each plate and write each number below. Then write how many are left.

2 — 1 = ___

2 cookies take away **1** cookie leaves **1** cookie.

  Count the cookies on each plate and write each number below. Then write how many are left.

___ — ___ = ___

4 cookies take away **2** cookies leaves **2** cookies.

Explore More

Practice subtraction like Cookie Monster! Place a few food items (like crackers, carrot sticks, or slices of cheese) on a plate. Have your child count how many are on the plate. Then, take some of the items away and have him count them again. Repeat the numbers as you practice and count. For example, you might say, "There were **4** crackers. I took away **2**, how many are left?"

151

Hip Hip Hooray for School! Learn About Math   **SESAME STREET**

Spring Cleaning

Bert is cleaning out his closet. He is going to give Oscar the socks with holes in them.

 Count all the socks on the path.

 Draw an **X** on the **2** socks with holes. Then circle the group that shows how many socks Bert has left.

Hip Hip Hooray for School! Learn About Math

Waiter Grover is at your service. Oh no!
There is a fly in the soup!

   Count all the bowls of soup. Draw an **X** on each bowl that has a fly in it. Count how many bowls are left and write the number.

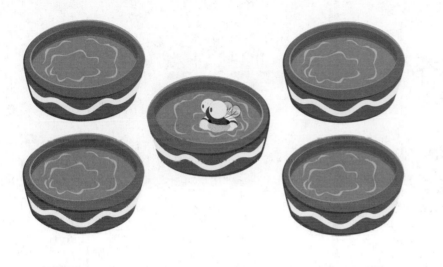

5 **–** **1** **=** _____
_ _ _ _ _ _ _
_____

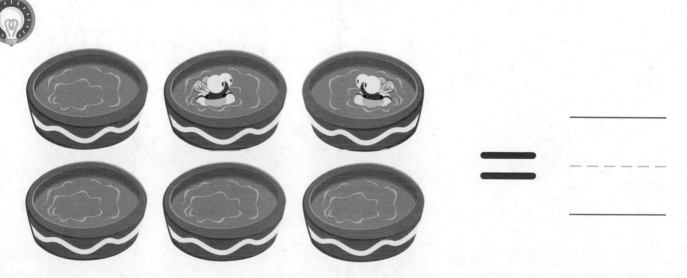

6 **–** **2** **=** _____
_ _ _ _ _ _ _
_____

153

Where Did All the Fish Go?

Ernie is swimming with some fish.
The **blue** fish keep swimming away.

 Count all the fish. Draw an **X** on the **blue** fish. Count how
many fish are left and write the number.

5 – 2 = _____

6 – 3 = _____

4 – 1 = _____

6 – 2 = _____

154

Hip Hip Hooray for School! Learn About Math

Ernie and Bert are playing outside. Zoe and Elmo want to play, too.

  Count the friends in each group and write each number below the picture. Write how many friends there are all together.

_____   **+**   _____   **=**   _____

Bert has to go home to feed Bernice.

   Count the friends. Circle the friend who is going home. Write how many friends will stay and play.

_____

Elmo is playing adding tic-tac-toe.

 Count the things in each group and write how many all together. Draw a line through three numbers that are the same.

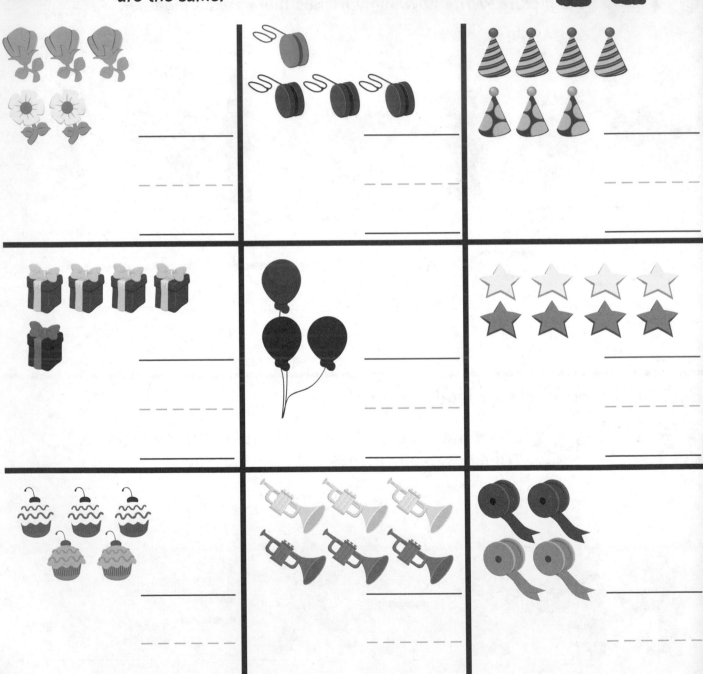

Great adding! You are a math champ! What else can you add?

SESAME STREET   Hip Hip Hooray for School! Learn About Math

Let's Celebrate!

Ernie and Bert want to celebrate all of your hard work. They want to have a party!

  Count the party balloons in each row and write the number to show how many.

_____
- - - - -
_____

_____
- - - - -
_____

  Now write how many party balloons there are all together. Then color all of the balloons.

_____
- - - - -
_____

Great adding!

(157)

Hip Hip Hooray for School! Learn About Math SESAME STREET

Zoe and Big Bird have made you a special party sign.

Trace the letters on the sign. Then write your name on the line.

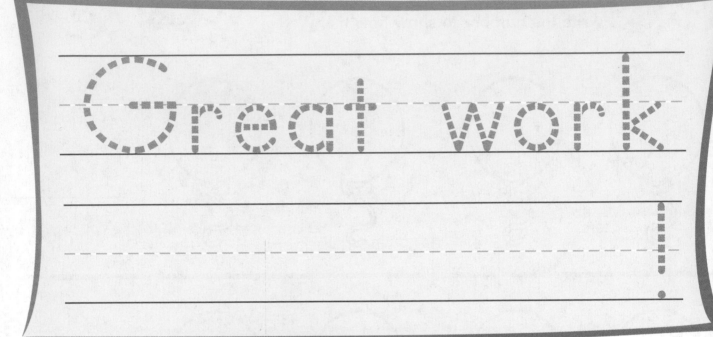

Great work!

Who else could celebrate with you?

  Draw and color yourself and some friends of your own.

 Now count how many friends there are all together at the party. Write the number.

_____

- - - - - - - - - - -

_____

159

Hip Hip Hooray for School! Learn About Math   SESAME STREET

Index